English

Assessment Papers

12+-13+ years

OXFORD

UNIVERSITY PRESS

Great Clarendon Street, Oxford, OX2 6DP, United Kingdom

Oxford University Press is a department of the University of Oxford.
It furthers the University's objective of excellence in research,
scholarship, and education by publishing worldwide. Oxford is a
registered trade mark of Oxford University Press in the UK and in
certain other countries

British Library Cataloguing in Publication Data
Data available

978-0-19-274009-0

10 9 8 7 6 5 4 3 2 1

Printed in China

Acknowledgements

The publishers would like to thank the following for permissions to
use copyright material

Page make-up: GreenGate Publishing Services, Tonbridge, Kent
Cover illustrations: Lo Cole

page 2 extract from 'My Great Aunt Appearing Day' by John Prebble, published
by Secker & Warburg. Reprinted by permission of The Random House Group
Ltd; page 35 extract from 'My Family and other Animals' by Gerald Durrell.
Reproduced with permission of Curtis Brown Group Ltd, London on behalf of
the Estate of Gerald Durrell. Copyright © Gerald Durrell 1956; page 9 extract
from 'Harbinger of death in steep decline' by Lewis Smith. Reproduced with
permission of The Times / NI Syndication; page 22 extract from 'The Discovery
of the Tomb of Tutankhamen' by Howard Carter and A C Mace. Reproduced
with permission of Dover Publications 1977; page 16 extract from 'Lord of the
Flies' by William Golding. Reproduced with permission of Faber and Faber Ltd,
1977.

Although we have made every effort to trace and contact all
copyright holders before publication this has not been possible in all
cases. If notified, the publisher will rectify any errors or omissions at
the earliest opportunity.

Links to third party websites are provided by Oxford in good faith
and for information only. Oxford disclaims any responsibility for
the materials contained in any third party website referenced in
this work.

Before you get started

What is Bond?

This book is part of the Bond Assessment Papers series for English, which provides **thorough and continuous practice of key English skills** from ages five to thirteen. Bond's English resources are ideal preparation for SATs exams, preparation for the 11+ and higher selective school entrance exams.

What does this book cover and how can it be used to prepare for exams?

English Assessment Papers 12+-13+ are intended as practice for 12+ and 13+ exams. The coverage is matched to the National Curriculum, so will provide invaluable preparation in the run-up to Key Stage 3 SATs. They can also be used for very advanced practice for selective exams at 11. Each paper practises comprehension, spelling, grammar and vocabulary work. It is outside the scope of this book to practise extended and creative writing skills. *Bond Focus on Writing* provides full coverage of writing skills.

What does the book contain?

- **10 papers** – each one contains 100 questions.

- **Tutorial links throughout** – – this icon appears in the margin next to the questions. It indicates links to the relevant section in *How to do ... 11+ English*. Our invaluable subject guide offers explanations and practice for all core question types that are commonly found on 11+, 12+ and 13+ exam papers.

- **Scoring devices** – there are score boxes in the margins and a Progress Chart on page 68. The chart is a visual and motivating way for children to see how they are doing. It also turns the score into a percentage that can help decide what to do next.

- **Next Steps Planner** – advice on what to do after finishing the papers can be found on the inside back cover.

- **Answers** – located in an easily-removed central pull-out section.

How can you use this book?

One of the great strengths of Bond Assessment Papers is their flexibility. They can be used at home, in school and by tutors to:

- set **timed formal practice tests** – allow about 50 minutes per paper in line with standard entrance exam demands. Reduce the suggested time limit by five minutes to practise working at speed.

- provide **bite-sized chunks** for regular practice.

- **highlight strengths and weaknesses** in the core skills.

- identify **individual needs**.

- set **homework**.

It is best to start at the beginning and work through the papers in order. If you are using the book as part of a careful run-in to an exam, we suggest that you also have three other essential Bond resources close at hand:

How to do 11+ English: the subject guide that explains the key question types practised in this book. Use the cross-reference icons to find the relevant sections.

Focus on Comprehension: the practical handbook that clearly shows children how to read and understand the text, understand the questions and assess their own answers.

Focus on Writing: the essential resource that explains the key components of successful writing.

See the inside front cover for more details of these books.

What does a score mean and how can it be improved?

It is unfortunately impossible to guarantee that a child will pass a 12+ or 13+ exam if they achieve a certain score on any practice book or paper. Success on the day depends on a host of factors, including the scores of the other children sitting the test. However, we can give some guidance on what a score indicates and how to improve it.

If children colour in the Progress Chart on page 68, this will give an idea of present performance in percentage terms. The Next Steps Planner inside the back cover will help you to decide what to do next to help a child progress. It is always valuable to go over wrong answers with children. If they are having trouble with a particular topic or skill, follow the tutorial links to *How to do ... 11+ English* for step-by-step explanations and further practice.

Don't forget the website...!

Visit www.bond11plus.co.uk for lots of advice, information and suggestions on everything to do with Bond and helping children to do their best.

Key words

Some special words are used in this book. You will find them in **bold** each time they appear in the Papers. These words are explained here.

abbreviation	a word or words which is/are shortened
abstract noun	a noun showing ideas, actions or qualities *dignity*
active verb	form of a verb showing when the main person or thing does the action *he <u>took</u> it*
adjectival clause	a clause giving information about a noun or pronoun
adjectival phrase	a group of words describing a noun
adjective	a word that describes somebody or something
adverb	a word that gives extra meaning to a verb
adverbial clause	a clause giving extra meaning to the main verb in a sentence
adverbial phrase	a phrase giving information about how, when, why and with whom something happens
antonym	a word with a meaning opposite to another word *hot – cold*
clause	a section of a sentence with a verb
collective noun	a word referring to a group *swarm*
definition	a meaning of a word
diminutive	a word implying smallness *booklet*
direct speech	words which show when someone is actually speaking
expression	a particular phrase or set used to express something
homophone	a word that has the same sound as another but a different meaning or spelling *right/write*
metaphor	an expression in which something is described in terms usually associated with another *the sky is a <u>sapphire sea</u>*
noun	a word for somebody or something
passive verb	form of a verb showing when the main person or thing has the action done to it *it <u>was taken</u> by him*
phrase	a group of words that act as a unit
plural	more than one *cats*
prefix	a group of letters added to the beginning of a word *un, dis*
preposition	a word that relates other words to each other *the book <u>on</u> the table*
pronoun	a word used to replace a noun *them*
reported speech	words which report something spoken after it has happened
root word	a word to which prefixes or suffixes can be added to make other words *<u>quickly</u>*
sentence	a unit of written language which makes sense by itself
simile	an expression to describe what something is like *as cold as ice*
singular	one *cat*
suffix	a group of letters added to the end of a word *ly, ful*
superlative	describes the limit of a quality (adjective or adverb) *most/least* or *shortest*
synonym	a word with the same or very similar meaning as another word *quick – fast*
verb	a 'doing' or 'being' word

My Great-Aunt Appearing Day

I was thirteen when I first heard of my great-aunt Appearing Day.

Late one afternoon, shortly after my birthday, my father discovered me at play with a crude bow and arrow I had fashioned for myself. For some minutes he watched me from the kitchen door, his hands thrust into the front pockets of his check trousers, his eyes squinting against the sun. Then he called me to him 5 abruptly, and when I came he took the toy from my hands. I waited, expecting a rebuke, but instead he slipped the bow back into my hand and said, 'Your great-aunt would like that.' Then he looked down at me with the warm and gentle smile of a man enjoying some secret humour.

Because he was a man who liked to make the most of the little dramas of life he 10 did not tell me immediately of my great-aunt, but chose to be mysterious. I cannot blame him for this. Being postmaster to a small Kentish village offered him little other excitement, and the story of Joshua Tanner and Appearing Day deserved the touch of theatre he gave to it. When he had returned the bow he took one hand from his pocket and gently fingered his watch-fob. 'Come with me, boy,' he said at 15 last. 'I'd like to show you something.'

We walked through the kitchen, through the dusty little post office to the street beyond. He kept his hands in his pockets and walked with great strides that outpaced mine, so that I hopped and skipped along behind him. We went up the street to the Norman church, and when we reached the gate he stopped and 20 played with his watch-fob again, watching me to see how I was responding to the mystery. 'Where would it be, now,' he said, winking slily to let me see that he knew all the time. My curiosity began to generate heat.

'Of course!' he said, and slapped his thigh, 'It's over there, beneath the cypresses.'

So off we went again, across the churchyard, threading our way past the little 25 hummocks of old graves, until we reached a lonely spot, almost overgrown with meadow-sweet and traveller's joy. I looked at it with some disappointment.

My father took a stick and carefully beat down the grass about the grave, and then he scratched the moss from the face of the stone. 'Can you read it?' he asked, looking over his shoulder at me. I could not, and said that I could not, with some 30 truculence, for I had expected more excitement than this. He straightened his back. 'Well then, I shall have to read it for you.' He traced the stick along the inscription on the stone, line by line. 'Here lies…' he said.

Here lies
JOSHUA TANNER 35
of this parish
Late Major of the United States Army
and his beloved wife
APPEARING DAY
a daughter of the Cheyenne, sister of the Arapaho 40
and a devout Christian
Joined in death October 14, 1894
'Nothing lives long, except the earth and the mountains'

When my father had finished reading he repeated the words *a daughter of the Cheyenne, sister of the Arapaho*. There was sadness in his voice, although he was smiling. Then once more he said the words *Cheyenne* and *Arapaho*, and made them sound like notes of some barbaric music. With his hands he gently moved the grass over the grave and threw the stick into the corner of the graveyard. He turned to face me. 'Well, what do you think of that?' 45

What was I to think, except that in this overgrown spot, twenty years before, had been buried two of my distant relatives? I considered this a very poor secret, and the expression on my face must have shown this, for my father's emotions suddenly exploded, blowing his hands out of those tight pockets and flinging them wide from his shoulders. 50

'An Indian, my boy!' he shouted triumphantly, 'A daughter of the Cheyenne. A real Indian buried here in Kent, and she was your great-aunt.' He placed his hand on my shoulder and the wonder of it came to me slowly. When he saw that my imagination was beginning to catch fire he whirled me about and set off smartly across the churchyard, through the creaking gate, down the village street. I trotted behind him, full of questions which were primarily concerned with whether this did or did not make me something of an Indian too. 55 60

From *Spanish Stirrup and Other Stories* by John Prebble

B

Answer these questions.

1 What would the author's great-aunt have liked?

_____

2 What was his father's job?

_____

3 Where did his father take him?

_____

4 What was the occupation of Joshua Tanner?

_____

5 What are the Cheyenne and the Arapaho?

_____

6 What does 'abruptly' mean (line 6)? _____

7–8 The author says he was 'expecting a rebuke' (lines 6–7). What does this remark tell you about the father and his relationship with his son?

_____

_____

9–10 How can you tell, in the second paragraph, that his father was also rather a kind man?

_____

_____

11–12 The author's father 'liked to make the most of the little dramas of life' (line 10). Explain what this means and why he did this.

_____

_____

13–15 Explain in your own words what the following mean:

a 'touch of theatre' (line 14) (*1 mark*)

_____

'My curiosity began to generate heat.' (*2 marks*)

_____

16 In what year is the author writing?

_____

17–18 Which two **adverbs** does the author use to show that his father treats the grave with respect?

_____

_____

19–20 Name two pieces of evidence in the passage which suggest that the churchyard is not well looked after.

_____

_____

_____

21–22 The author's father experiences two emotions when he reads and says the words 'Cheyenne' and 'Arapaho'. Explain what he feels and why you think he feels like this.

_____

_____

_____

23–24 Explain what the author means when he says: 'my imagination was beginning to catch fire' (lines 57–8).

_____

_____

25–26 How do you know that the author's father likes secrets and mysteries? Give two examples from the passage.

_____

_____

27–28 How do you know that the author was at first unimpressed by what his father showed him? Answer with reference to two parts of the passage.

_____

_____

29–30 Who do you think the watch-fob might have once belonged to? Why?

_____

_____

○ 30

Match each word with its **definition** as used in the passage. Write the correct letter on the answer line.

E 2

31 crude (line 3)	_____	(a) defiance
32 fashioned (line 3)	_____	(b) firstly
33 rebuke (line 7)	_____	(c) small mounds
34 hummocks (line 26)	_____	(d) words on monument
35 truculence (line 31)	_____	(e) fierce/cruel
36 inscription (line 32)	_____	(f) made
37 devout (line 41)	_____	(g) rough/basic
38 barbaric (line 47)	_____	(h) earnestly religious
39 triumphantly (line 55)	_____	(i) telling off
40 primarily (line 60)	_____	(j) exultantly

○ 10

Explain what these **expressions** mean.

41–42 a golden boy

_____

_____

43–44 a half-baked boy

_____

_____

45–46 a mother's boy

_____

_____

47–48 a whipping boy

_____

_____

49–50 the boys in blue

_____

_____

10

E 2

Complete each word with 'le', 'el', or 'al'.

51 eas_____   **52** symmetric_____

53 peop_____   **54** origin_____

55 person_____   **56** mirac_____

57 perpetu_____   **58** satch_____

59 parall_____   **60** vow_____

10

Complete the table.

	Adjective	Adverb	Noun
61–62			curiosity
63–64			disappointment
65–66		abruptly	
67–68		luckily	
69–70	warm		

Complete each **sentence** by choosing the correct word from the brackets.

71 My father (allowed/aloud) _____ me to keep the bow and arrow.

72 Just after my thirteenth birthday he (choose/chose) _____ to tell me about my great-aunt.

73 The inscription was written on the (coarse/course) _____ stone.

74 The (sauce/source) _____ of the mystery was revealed.

75 It was quite a surprise to learn about my (past/passed) _____.

Complete each word with 're' or 'er'.

76 cent_____   77 scann_____

78 centimet_____   79 perimet_____

80 fib_____   81 thermomet_____

82 lit_____   83 gen_____

84 timb_____   85 diamet_____

Use a word or **phrase** to define these.

86 outpace   _____

87 outmoded   _____

88 outcome   _____

89 outwit   _____

90 outlay   _____

Complete the table.

		+ ing	+ ed
91–92	bury		
93–94	trace		
95–96	quarrel		
97–98	reveal		
99–100	incur		

10

Now go to the Progress Chart to record your score! **Total** 100

THE TIMES

TUESDAY SEPTEMBER 26 2006

Harbinger of death in steep decline

By Lewis Smith, Environment Reporter

BARN OWLS, emblematic of the country idyll, have suffered a catastrophic drop in numbers, with up to 75 per cent feared to have been wiped out.

A cold March and a wet May combined 5 to kill off parent birds and create appalling breeding conditions for survivors, the Barn Owl Trust said yesterday. Attempts by the birds to recover by raising late broods were ruined by repeated downpours last month. 10

Fewer than one in four regular breeding sites has been occupied this year in much of the country, and in Shropshire the figure fell to one in twelve.

"It's the worst year ever known," David 15 Ramsden, the head of conservation at the trust, said. He blamed changing weather patterns caused by global warming. "We were very optimistic things were generally picking up but this year has been a huge 20 setback. We aren't just talking about a few less pairs, we are talking about an incredible number less."

Farmers and other barn owners have been so alarmed at the struggle the birds 25 have faced to survive that they have been leaving out food.

Barn owls are harbingers of death in folklore and literature. Shakespeare, Byron, Jonson, Wordsworth and Keats all linked 30 the bird with death or misery.

Now the population has slumped well below the 4,000 pairs recorded in Britain in 1998. It had fallen in England and Wales by 69 per cent from 1932, when 12,142 35 pairs were recorded, to 1985 when 3,778 pairs were surveyed.

Population levels were thought to have stabilised from the 1980s and, since 1998, it was believed that numbers were 40 recovering. But this year's figures have set back conservation efforts by at least a decade.

Mr Ramsden added: "There may be as few as a thousand pairs breeding 45 this year in the whole of the UK. That's catastrophic. The numbers are lower than ten years ago. Almost every year has record-breaking weather and prolonged extreme conditions are bad news for barn 50 owls. The thought that climate change may significantly hinder the recovery of this national treasure is a huge worry to those concerned with barn owl conservation."

Mr Ramsden has been monitoring sites 55 in Devon and collating findings from surveys elsewhere. In Devon only 15 of the 72 regularly monitored nest sites were occupied this year. Most or all would normally be used by the birds and their 60 absence has been repeated in many other countries. A cold March meant that the small mammals on which barn owls prey, particularly voles, were in short supply. Many adults starved to death. The number 65 of dead owls reported in early spring was three times higher than usual.

Persistent rain in May forced the birds to restrict their hunting because the feathers that enable the owl to fly 70 silently get waterlogged easily.

A further sign of an appalling year is the lack of reports this month of owls being struck by vehicles. About 75 per cent of barn owls that die in their first year 75 are killed in this way.

Monitors for the British Trust for Ornithology also reported disastrous results for the owl this year. David Leech, for the BTO, said that the bird had suffered 80

Answer these questions.

1–3 These statistics are used in the newspaper report. To what do they refer?

(a) 'well below 4,000'

_____

(b) '12,142'

_____

(c) '72'

_____

4 How many breeding sites in Shropshire were occupied this year?

_____

5 Were there more or fewer than a thousand breeding pairs of barn owls ten years ago?

_____

6 How many breeding sites in Devon have not been used this year?

_____

7 What does BTO stand for?

_____

8–9 What were the weather conditions like in:

March: _____

May: _____

10–11 How did conditions in these months specifically affect the barn owls?

March: _____

_____

May: _____

_____

12 How can you tell that farmers quite like barn owls?

_____

13 During which decade did barn owl numbers stop going down?

_____

14 Discuss whether the decline of barn owls is unique to Britain.

_____

15–16 In August 2006:

    (a)   What was the weather like?

    _____

    (b)   How did it affect the barn owls?

    _____

17–18 Explain what these **expressions** mean.

    (a)   'harbingers of death' (line 28)

    _____

    (b)   'thought to have stabilised' (lines 38–9)

    _____

19 Why do you think it is important for the owls to be able to fly silently?

_____

_____

20–21 How is a 'lack of reports this month of owls being struck by vehicles' a 'further sign of an appalling year'?

_____

_____

22–24 Explain in your own words: 'emblematic of the country idyll' (lines 1–2).

_____

_____

25–27 Find three pieces of evidence in the newspaper report that suggest people care about what happens to barn owls.

_____

_____

_____

28–30 The newspaper reports three sources which confirm the declining number of barn owls. What are they?

(a) _____

(b) _____

(c) _____

Match each word with its **definition** as it is used in the newspaper report.

31 appalling _____   (a) analysing

32 regular _____   (b) extended

33 optimistic _____   (c) continuing

34 incredible _____   (d) shocking

35 slumped _____   (e) usual

36 surveyed _____   (f) hard to believe

37 prolonged _____   (g) fallen

38 significantly _____   (h) investigated

39 collating _____   (i) hopeful

40 persistent _____   (j) considerably

Complete each **sentence**.

41 Ornithology is the scientific study of _____.

42 Palaeontology is the scientific study of _____.

43 Climatology is the scientific study of _____.

44 Zoology is the scientific study of _____.

45 Pathology is the scientific study of _____.

Complete each word with 'or' or 'ar'.

46 irregul_____   47 auth_____

48 denominat_____   49 supervis_____

50 triangul_____   51 perpendicul_____

52 metaph_____   **53** regulat_____

54 muscul_____   **55** famili_____

10

D 6

Replace the words in bold with a single **adverb**.

56 Mr Ramsden spoke of the plight of the barn owl **with dejection**.

_____

57 The number of the birds had been counted **with precision**.

_____

58 Rain in May fell **with persistence**.

_____

59 The Trust reported **with optimism** on the number of breeding pairs.

_____

60 'We are unable to improve the situation for the owls,' he said **with candour**.

_____

5

Change these **sentences** from active to passive.

D 1

61 David Ramsden blamed global warming.

_____

62 Extreme weather conditions affect the barn owls.

_____

63 Farmers have left food out for the owls.

_____

64 Monitors reported disastrous results this year.

_____

65 When an owl sees a shrew or a mouse, it drops with talons outspread.

_____

5

Make each **verb** into an **abstract noun** ending in 'tion' or 'sion'.

66 create   _____

67 add   _____

68 conclude   _____

69 invade   _____

70 evaluate   _____

71 comprehend   _____

72 suspend   _____

73 celebrate   _____

74 solve   _____

75 collide   _____

10

Explain what these **expressions** mean.

76–77 a bird of ill-omen

_____

_____

78–79 to be able to charm the birds off the trees

_____

_____

80–81 a bird in the hand is worth two in the bush

_____

_____

82–83 to kill two birds with one stone

_____

_____

84–85 birds of a feather flock together

_____

_____

10

In each **sentence**, change the **verb** in bold to a **noun**. Rewrite the **sentences** accordingly.

D 1
D 6

86 Barn owls **prey** on voles.

_____

87 Cold and wet weather **combined** to kill off parent birds.

_____

88 The numbers of pairs **were surveyed** in 1985.

_____

89 The birds **had suffered** particularly badly in the South West.

_____

90 The population **has slumped** alarmingly.

_____

5

E 2

Write a **phrase** to explain the meaning of these words.

91 decade _____

92 decathlon _____

93 decagon _____

94 decapod _____

95 decahedron _____

5

E 2

Complete each **sentence** with the correct **homophone** from the brackets.

96 The (practice/practise) _____ of monitoring the birds goes on every year.

97 The extreme weather is the (principle/principal) _____ cause of the declining bird numbers.

98 The small mammals on which barn owls (prey/pray) _____ are in short supply.

99 The owls are (dependant/dependent) _____ on small mammals for their food.

100 We would (counsel/council) _____ all farmers to put out food for the owls in these difficult times.

5

The boy with fair hair lowered himself down the last few feet of rock and began to pick his way towards the lagoon. Though he had taken off his school sweater and trailed it now from one hand, his grey shirt stuck to him and his hair was plastered to his forehead. All round him the long scar smashed into the jungle was a bath of heat. He was clambering heavily among the creepers and broken trunks when a   5 bird, a vision of red and yellow, flashed upwards with a witch-like cry; and this cry was echoed by another.

"Hi!" it said, "wait a minute!"

The undergrowth at the side of the scar was shaken and a multitude of raindrops fell pattering.   10

"Wait a minute," the voice said, "I got caught up."

The fair boy stopped and jerked his stockings with an automatic gesture that made the jungle seem for a moment like the Home Counties.

The voice spoke again.

"I can't hardly move with all these creeper things."   15

The owner of the voice came backing out of the undergrowth so that twigs scratched on a greasy wind-breaker. The naked crooks of his knees were plump, caught and scratched by thorns. He bent down, removed the thorns carefully, and turned round. He was shorter than the fair boy and very fat. He came forward, searching out safe lodgements for his feet, and then looked up through thick spectacles.   20

"Where's the man with the megaphone?"

The fair boy shook his head.

"This is an island. At least I think it's an island. That's a reef out in the sea. Perhaps there aren't any grown-ups anywhere."

The fat boy looked startled.   25

"There was that pilot. But he wasn't in the passenger tube, he was up in the cabin in front."

The fair boy was peering at the reef through screwed-up eyes.

"All them other kids," the fat boy went on. "Some of them must have got out. They must have, mustn't they?"   30

The fair boy began to pick his way as casually as possible towards the water. He tried to be offhand and not too obviously uninterested but the fat boy hurried after him.

"Aren't there any grown-ups at all?"

"I don't think so."

The fair boy said this solemnly; but then the delight of a realized ambition   35 overcame him. In the middle of the scar he stood on his head and grinned at the reversed fat boy.

"No grown-ups!"

The fat boy thought for a moment.

"That pilot."   40

The fair boy allowed his feet to come down and sat on the steamy earth.

"He must have flown off after he dropped us. He couldn't land here. Not in a plane with wheels."

"We was attacked!"

"He'll be back all right."   45

The fat boy shook his head.

"When we was coming down I looked through one of them windows. I saw the other part of the plane. There were flames coming out of it."

He looked up and down the scar.

"And this is what the tube done." 50

The fair boy reached out and touched the jagged end of a trunk. For a moment he looked interested.

"What happened to it?" he asked. "Where's it got to now?"

"That storm dragged it out to sea. It wasn't half dangerous with all them tree trunks falling. There must have been some kids still in it." 55

He hesitated for a moment then spoke again.

"What's your name?"

"Ralph."

The fat boy waited to be asked his name in turn but this proffer of acquaintance was not made; the fair boy called Ralph smiled vaguely, stood up, and began to 60 make his way once more towards the lagoon. The fat boy hung steadily at his shoulder.

"I expect there's a lot more of us scattered about. You haven't seen any others have you?"

Ralph shook his head and increased his speed. Then he tripped over a branch and came down with a crash. 65

The fat boy stood by him, breathing hard.

"My auntie told me not to run," he explained, "on account of my asthma."

"Ass-mar?"

"That's right. Can't catch me breath. I was the only boy in our school what had asthma," said the fat boy with a touch of pride. "And I've been wearing specs since I 70 was three."

From *Lord of the Flies* by William Golding

Answer these questions.

1 What was the fair-haired boy wearing?

_____

2 How was the boy who came out of the undergrowth different from the fair-haired boy?

_____

3 Which two adults did they think might be on the island?

_____

4 Why does the fat boy think that the plane has been attacked?

_____

_____

5 What **metaphor** does the author use to give the impression of how hot it was?

_____

17

6 How does the author suggest in the first paragraph that the jungle is a rather sinister place?

_____

7 Explain what the fat boy meant when he said, 'I got caught up' (line 11).

_____

8–9 Find two pieces of evidence in the text which suggest that the weather had been bad.

_____

_____

10 What do you think the 'passenger tube' was?

_____

11–12 What was the 'realized ambition' (line 35) that came over Ralph?

_____

_____

13–14 How do you know that it was difficult for Ralph to move towards the lagoon? Give two examples to explain your answer.

_____

_____

15–16 How do you know that:

(a)   the fat boy was uncomfortable at the thought of no adults on the island?

_____

(b)   Ralph was pleased that there were no adults on the island?

_____

17–19 Give three reasons why the fat boy thinks that the pilot won't be coming back.

_____

_____

_____

20–22 (a)   Which of the boys is anxious to know if there are any other survivors? (*1 mark*)

_____

(b) Give two examples from the passage to explain your answer. (*2 marks*)

_____

_____

23–24 Explain in your own words what 'this proffer of acquaintance' (line 59) means.

_____

25–27 How do you know that Ralph is not interested in being friends with the fat boy? Give examples from the text to explain your answer.

_____

_____

28–30 Describe the personality of the fat boy in your own words.

_____

_____

(30

Match each word with its **definition** as used in the passage.

E 2

31 multitude   _____   (a) offer

32 automatic   _____   (b) seriously

33 lodgements   _____   (c) without thinking

34 solemnly   _____   (d) safe places

35 proffer   _____   (e) a great many

(5

Complete the **verb** table.

D 6

	he flies	he flew	he has flown
36	he draws		
37	he goes		
38	he writes		
39	he swims		
40	he grows		
41	he comes		
42	he drives		
43	he gives		
44	he is		
45	he speaks		

(10

Complete each word with 'ance' or 'ence'.

46 resembl_____

47 entr_____

48 evid_____

49 conveni_____

50 perform_____

51 abs_____

52 repugn_____

53 audi_____

54 resist_____

55 obedi_____

Explain what these **expressions** mean.

56–57 to pour oil on troubled waters

_____

58–59 to pour cold water on something

_____

60–61 to be dull as ditchwater

_____

62–63 to be in hot water

_____

64–65 water under the bridge

_____

Solve the clues with 'ph' words.

66 funnel-shaped hand-held device for making the voice louder _____

67 a musical instrument _____

68 a fear of open spaces _____

69 a comparison where something is said to be something else _____

70 a terrible disaster _____

Write these **sentences** correctly.

D 1

71 'We was attacked!'

_____

72–73 'When we was coming down I looked through one of them windows.'

_____

74 'Can't catch me breath.'

_____

75 'I was the only boy in our school what had asthma.'

_____

5

E 2

Add 'a', 'ai', 'ei' or 'ay' to complete each word.

76 w_____ght

77 str_____ght

78 persu_____de

79 all_____

80 oct_____ve

81 r_____gn

82 cont_____n

83 sl_____gh

84 del_____

85 st_____d

10

D 6

Write V (**verb**) or A (**adjective**) for each word in bold.

86 The **dripping** raindrops pattered around him. _____

87 The raindrops were **dripping** from the trees. _____

88 The **squawking** bird flew overhead. _____

89 **Squawking** noisily, the bird flew away. _____

90 Ralph was **grinning** as he stood on his head. _____

91 The **grinning** boy stood on his head. _____

6

Write **antonyms** for these words.

92 increased   _____

93 lowered   _____

94 heavily   _____

95 uninterested   _____

96 dangerous   _____

97 vaguely   _____

98 spacious   _____

99 stingy   _____

100 logical   _____

9

Now go to the Progress Chart to record your score!   Total 100

Paper 4

Howard Carter was an archaeologist who excavated in the Valley of the Kings in Egypt. This is an extract from his autobiography when he discovered the tomb of Tutankhamen in 1922.

This was to be our final season in The Valley. Six full seasons we had excavated there, and season after season had drawn a blank; we had worked for months at a stretch and found nothing, and only an excavator knows how desperately depressing that can be; we had almost made up our minds that we were beaten, and were preparing to leave The Valley and try our luck elsewhere; and then 5
– hardly had we set hoe to ground in our last despairing effort than we made a discovery that far exceeded our wildest dreams. Surely, never before in the whole history of excavation has a full digging season been compressed within the space of five days.

    Let me try and tell the story of it all. It will not be easy, for the dramatic 10
suddenness of the initial discovery left me in a dazed condition, and the months that have followed have been so crowded with incident that I have hardly had time to think. Setting it down on paper will perhaps give me a chance to realize what has happened and all that it means.

I arrived in Luxor on October 28th, and by November 1st I had enrolled my 15
workmen and was ready to begin. Our former excavations had stopped short
at the north-east corner of the tomb of Rameses VI, and from this point I started
trenching southwards. It will be remembered that in this area there were a number
of roughly constructed workmen's huts, used probably by the labourers in the tomb
of Rameses… After we had planned and noted them, they were removed, and we 20
were ready to clear away the three feet of soil that lay beneath them.

Hardly had I arrived on the work the next morning (November 4th) than the
unusual silence, due to the stoppage of work, made me realize that something out
of the ordinary had happened, and I was greeted by the announcement that a steep
cut in the rock had been discovered underneath the very first hut to be attacked. 25
This seemed too good to be true, but a short amount of extra clearing revealed the
fact that we were actually in the entrance of a steep cut in the rock, some thirteen
feet below the entrance to the tomb of Rameses VI, and a similar depth from the
present bed level of The Valley. The manner of cutting was that of a sunken stairway
entrance so common in The Valley, and I almost dared to hope that we had 30
found our tomb at last. Work continued feverishly throughout the whole of that day
and the morning of the next, but it was not until the afternoon of November 5th that
we succeeded in clearing away the masses of rubbish that overlay the cut, and
were able to demarcate the upper edges of the stairway on all four sides.

It was clear by now beyond any question that we actually had before us the 35
entrance to a tomb, but doubts, born of previous disappointments, persisted in
creeping in. There was always the horrible possibility, suggested by our experience
in the Thothmes III Valley, that the tomb was an unfinished one, never completed
and never used: if it had been finished there was the depressing possibility that it
had been completely plundered in ancient times. On the other hand, there was just 40
the chance of an untouched or only partially plundered tomb, and it was with ill-
suppressed excitement that I watched the descending steps of the staircase, as one
by one they came to light. The cutting was excavated in the side of a small hillock,
and, as the work progressed, its western edge receded under the slope of the rock
until it was, first partially, and then completely, roofed in, and became a passage, 45
10 feet high by 6 feet wide. Work progressed more rapidly now; step succeeded
step, and at the level of the twelfth, towards sunset, there was disclosed the upper
part of a doorway, blocked, plastered and sealed.

A sealed doorway – it was actually true, then! Our years of patient labour were to
be rewarded after all, and I think my first feeling was one of congratulation that my 50
faith in The Valley had not been unjustified.

From *The Discovery of the Tomb of Tutankhamen* by Howard Carter and A C Mace

Answer these questions.

Write T (true) or F (false) against each statement.

1 Carter had been excavating in the Valley of the Kings for six seasons. _____

2 Carter arrived in Luxor on November 1st. _____

3 The area Carter was interested in was covered with workmen's huts. _____

4 A steep cut into the rock was discovered under the third hut to be cleared away. _____

5 The discovered tomb had been completely plundered in ancient times. _____

6 A 'season' in the Valley of the Kings ran from October to March. Why do you think Carter only worked during these months?

_____

7 What was special about Carter's digging season?

_____

_____

8–11 Explain what these **expressions** mean.

drawn a blank _____

out of the ordinary _____

too good to be true _____

beyond any question _____

12 How did the workmen's huts hamper Carter's work?

_____

_____

13 How do you know that the excavation site was usually noisy and busy?

_____

_____

14 How many steps did the workmen uncover? _____

15–16 Where had Carter excavated before and why had it been a disappointing experience?

_____

_____

17–20 What do these words mean?

'demarcate' (line 34) _____

'ill-suppressed' (lines 41–2) _____

'trenching' (line 18) _____

'persisted' (line 36) _____

21–22 Describe how Carter was feeling at the beginning of the extract. Quote from the extract to support your answer.

_____

_____

23–24 Write in your own words what Carter hoped to achieve by writing about his find.

_____

_____

25–26 Explain in your own words the two main reasons why Carter wrote 'it will not be easy' to tell the story of the discovery.

_____

_____

27–28 Why do you think Carter uses the word 'feverishly' to describe the work after the first step had been uncovered?

_____

_____

29–30 Carter was sure he had found the entrance to a tomb but 'doubts … persisted in creeping in'. Explain in your own words why he had doubts and what they were.

_____

_____

_____

31 How can you tell that, although Carter had doubts, he was still optimistic?

_____

_____

32 What was the sure sign that a tomb had not been plundered?

_____

33 What time of day did Carter realise that the tomb had not been robbed?

_____

34–35 Explain in your own words what Carter's main emotions were when he discovered the sealed doorway.

_____

_____ ⬤ 35

Write the **synonym** for each word as it is used in the extract. Begin with the given initial letter.

〔D〕〔9〕

36 constructed	b_____	
37 labourers	w_____	
38 revealed	s_____	
39 faith	b_____	
40 endeavoured	t_____	
41 compressed	s_____	
42 enrolled	h_____	
43 plundered	r_____	
44 former	p_____	
45 feverishly	f_____	⬤ 10

〔E〕〔2〕

Complete the table.

	Adjective	Comparative	Superlative
46	wild		
47	rough		
48	dramatic		
49	unusual		
50	gloomy		
51	good		
52	bad		
53	low		⬤ 8

Explain what these **expressions** mean.

54–55 to discuss something behind closed doors

_____

56–57 to show someone the door

_____

58–59 to let something in through the back door

_____

60–61 to lay something at someone's door

_____

62–63 to lock the stable door after the horse has bolted

_____ (10

The missing letter or letters in these words make the sound 'sh'. Add: 't', 's', 'ch', 'ss' or 'ci' to complete each word.

E 2

64 loca_____ion   **65** vi_____ion

66 excur_____ion   **67** vaca_____ion

68 pa_____ion   **69** edi_____ion

70 omi_____ion   **71** profi_____ent

72 _____auffeur   **73** interroga_____ion   (10

Write the **diminutive** of each word.

D 8

74 hill   _____

75 book   _____

76 note   _____

77 statue   _____

78 grain   _____   (5

(27)

Write whether each word in bold is an **adjective**, **adverb** or a **noun**.

79 The **danger** of running out of money was very real. _____

80 Carter was **dangerously** close to running out of money.

_____

81 Carter found himself in a **dangerous** situation. _____

82 They removed the huts **carefully**. _____

83 The **careful** workmen removed the huts. _____

84 The workmen removed the huts with **care**. _____

85 Carter said the measurements must be **exact**. _____

86 They measured the uncovered step **exactly**. _____

87 The **exactness** of the measurement was important. _____

88 What they found in the tomb was **magnificent**. _____

89 Some of the objects were **magnificently** decorated. _____

90 The **magnificence** of the tomb astonished Carter. _____

Complete each word with 'ent' or 'ant'.

91 depend_____   92 instrum_____

93 transpar_____   94 hesit_____

95 perman_____   96 irrelev_____

97 defici_____   98 stagn_____

99 leni_____   100 poign_____

Many famous stories have their origins in the mists of time. They tell of brave heroes, daring deeds, unspeakable monsters and impossible quests. One such story is Theseus and the Minotaur.

According to legend, there lived, under the magnificent palace in Crete, a monster known as the Minotaur. This fearsome creature had the body of a huge man and   5
the head of a bull. Its rapacious appetite could only be sated by human flesh and his thirst slaked by human blood. King Minos of Crete satisfied the monster with youths and maidens from the lands he conquered.

When King Aegeus was in the unhappy position of sending human sacrifices to appease the ravening monster, his son, Theseus, stated his intention to be one   10
of the victims. He declared that he would slay the beast or share the fate of his countrymen and women.

Aegeus trembled with foreboding. He did not want his son to go but Theseus was adamant. 'If I conquer the Minotaur,' he said, 'never again will our people have to meet this horrifying fate.'   15

In the face of his son's determination, Aegeus had no option but to agree. He was proud of his son's bravery and buried his fear deep in his heart. 'The ship you will voyage in to death or glory will bear black sails. Should you be victorious in your quest, hoist white sails on your return so we can prepare the celebrations. If the ship returns to our harbour with sails unchanged, we will know that all have   20
perished in the labyrinthine tomb.'

Theseus promised this and knelt before him for his blessing. Their formal farewell belied the depth of their sorrow at parting in this way.

A melancholy voyage brought Theseus and the other victims to the shores of Crete. They were escorted with ceremony to the palace which was to be their   25
prison, where fate intervened in the form of Ariadne, daughter of King Minos. Seeing Theseus' bravery and regal bearing, she fell immediately in love with him and determined to save him or die in the attempt.

In the dead of night, Ariadne stole through the cavernous halls of the palace to where Theseus was imprisoned. 'You must follow my instructions exactly,' she   30
whispered to him. 'At daybreak, you will be escorted to the Labyrinth. Make sure you are the first to enter. Conceal this ball of thread about your person. When the door of the Labyrinth is closed on you, tie one end to the door. Unroll it as you go so it will serve as a means of escape. I will conceal myself near the entrance and let you out should you prevail.'   35

Theseus felt a dim flickering of optimism as he listened intently to her words. The echoing sound of footsteps startled them both. 'It is the guard,' Theseus hissed. 'You must leave!'

'I will, but you must make me a promise. Swear on the life we are trying to preserve!'

'Anything,' Theseus whispered fervently, 'but hurry.'   40

'If you survive the ordeal the gods have decreed you must face, you must ensure my survival. If ever my father discovered I had aided you to defeat the Minotaur, my life would be forfeit.'

'You will be on my ship and safe before our plan is discovered,' he assured her. Now go!'   45

Sleep eluded Theseus that night and, at the first paling of the eastern sky, he found himself alone in the Labyrinth. The chill of the rough, stone walls seeped into his bones and he felt a thin film of sweat on his skin. The blood pounded in his ears. He secured the thread and began the tortuous journey to the centre of the maze. A low, blood-curdling growl from the monster guided Theseus to its lair. Nothing had prepared him for the sight he encountered which made the very blood freeze in his veins and, momentarily, robbed him of his wits. The Minotaur fell silent. Man and monster locked eyes. Then, with speed belying its huge bulk, the monster flung himself at Theseus. 50

He regained his wits in time to land a forceful punch on the monster's heart. He leapt aside and when the monster attacked again, he repeated the blow. Over and over, Theseus pounded until the Minotaur was visibly weakened. He then seized his opportunity as the monster staggered in pain and anger. With a defiant shout, Theseus leapt on to the Minotaur's back, grabbed its hideous horns and, summoning the last of his strength, wrenched the creature's head back. The sickening crack of its breaking neck echoed through the maze. Theseus leapt aside as the gargantuan body smashed to the ground. 55 60

Theseus stood, looking at the dead monster with horror and fascination until some ethereal voice in his head urged him to flee. The living nightmare was not yet over.

He pressed his body to the wall and edged towards the opening. Once outside the Minotaur's tomb, he began to think clearly. He fumbled for the thread and retraced his steps. Flinging himself on the door, he pounded with what remained of his strength. 65

Ariadne was true to her word. Wrenching open the door, she dragged Theseus from the realms of death into the warmth of the sunlight. 70

B

Answer these questions.

1 What was the colour of the sails of the boat which took Theseus to Crete?

_____

2 Where did Minos rule?

_____

3 What promise did Theseus make to Ariadne?

_____

4 What time of day did Theseus enter the Labyrinth?

_____

5 What did the Minotaur look like?

_____

6–7 How did Aegeus feel when Theseus said he wanted to go to Crete to fight the Minotaur?

_____

_____

8–9 Explain in your own words why Ariadne fell in love with Theseus. Give two reasons.

_____

_____

10 Why do you think Ariadne instructed Theseus to go into the Labyrinth first?

_____

_____

11–12 In what two ways could Theseus meet his death?

_____

_____

13–14 What was Ariadne frightened about?

_____

_____

15 Underline the word you think best describes Ariadne.

romantic   resourceful   slow-witted

16–17 Find two pieces of evidence from the passage to support your answer above.

_____

_____

18 Underline the word you think best describes Theseus.

cowardly   stupid   valiant

19–20 Find two pieces of evidence from the passage to support your answer above.

_____

_____

21–23 Explain in your own words the three stages by which Theseus weakened and killed the Minotaur.

_____

_____

_____ 23

Circle the **definition** which is closest in meaning to the word in bold as it is used in the passage. E 2

24 hoist	put up	buy	make
25 blow	insult	punch	waft
26 labyrinth	palace	race	maze
27 prevail	suffer	win	lose
28 flee	escape	wandering	walk
29 blessing	gift	support	speech
30 intention	fear	luck	proposal
31 stole	moved stealthily	took unlawfully	crawled

8

D 9

Find **antonyms** in the passage for these words.

32 defeated _____

33 survived _____

34 ashamed _____

35 concealed _____

36 cowardice _____ 5

Write these as **adjectives** which end in the **suffix** 'some'.

D 6

E 2

37 inclined to argue _____

38 daring, inclined to take risks _____

39 pure, natural _____

40 causing fear _____

41 tedious and irritating _____ 5

Complete each word with 'oy' or 'oi'.

42 v_____ce

43 tabl_____d

44 _____ster

45 empl_____ment

46 m_____sture

47 dec_____

48 b_____cott

49 all_____

50 expl_____t

51 embr_____l

Add the missing commas in each **sentence**.

52–53 Theseus thought he would need a helmet a shield a net and a sword to defeat the Minotaur.

54–55 'You must do as I tell you' said Ariadne 'and you will succeed.'

56–57 The Labyrinth built by Minos was the home of the Minotaur.

58 Theseus broke the Minotaur's neck killing it instantly.

59 The other victims made their way to the ship crept quietly aboard and sailed away.

Write an **adjective** based on each of these **nouns**.

60 misery _____

61 pain _____

62 monster _____

63 hunger _____

64 doom _____

Explain what these **expressions** mean.

65–66 to breathe down someone's neck

_____

67–68 to get it in the neck

_____

69–70 to stick one's neck out

_____

71–72 to be neck and neck

_____

73–74 to be up to one's neck

_____

10

E 2

Write a 'sch' word for each of these clues.

    75 a place where you go to learn _____

    76 a type of sailing ship _____

    77 a plan showing the times for doing things _____

    78 a plan to get rich quick _____

    79 someone who is very learned _____

5

D 6

Complete the table.

	Adjective	Adverb	Noun
80–81	bold		
82–83	violent		
84–85	brave		
86–87	wicked		
88–89	prudent		

10

E 2

Write a **homophone** for each of these words.

    90 due _____

    91 court _____

    92 great _____

    93 canvas _____

    94 manner _____

    95 beat _____

6

Underline the **adjectival clause** in each **sentence**.

96 Theseus, who was the son of Aegeus, lived in Athens.

97 They sailed in a ship which had black sails.

98 Ariadne, who fell in love with Theseus, decided to help him.

99 She gave Theseus a ball of thread with which he could find his way out of the Labyrinth.

100 Theseus saw the Minotaur who was bellowing with rage.

5

Now go to the Progress Chart to record your score!   Total   100

Paper 6

Gerald Durrell writes of his childhood in My Family and Other Animals. *In this extract he is particularly interested in the scorpions which live in the crumbling wall which surrounds the garden.*

Then one day I found a fat female scorpion in the wall, wearing what at first glance appeared to be a pale fawn fur coat. Closer inspection proved that this strange garment was made up of a mass of tiny babies clinging to the mother's back. I was enraptured by this family, and I made up my mind to smuggle them into the house and up to my bedroom so that I might keep them and watch them grow up.   5
With infinite care I manoeuvred the mother and family into a matchbox, and then hurried to the villa. It was rather unfortunate that just as I entered the door lunch should be served; however, I placed the matchbox carefully on the mantelpiece in the drawing-room, so that the scorpions should get plenty of air, and made my way to the dining-room and joined the family for the meal. Dawdling over my food,   10
feeding Roger surreptitiously under the table and listening to the family arguing, I completely forgot about my exciting new captures. At last Larry, having finished, fetched the cigarettes from the drawing room, and lying back in his chair he put one in his mouth and picked up the matchbox he had brought. Oblivious of my impending doom I watched him interestedly as, still talking glibly, he opened the matchbox.   15
Now I maintain to this day that the female scorpion meant no harm. She was agitated and a trifle annoyed at being shut up in a matchbox for so long, and so she seized the first opportunity to escape. She hoisted herself out of the box with great rapidity, her babies clinging on desperately, and scuttled on to the back of Larry's hand. There, not quite certain what to do next, she paused, her sting curved   20
up at the ready. Larry, feeling the movement of her claws, glanced down to see what it was, and from that moment things got increasingly confused.

He uttered a roar of fright that made Lugaretzia drop a plate and brought Roger
out from beneath the table, barking wildly. With a flick of his hand he sent the
unfortunate scorpion flying down the table, and she landed midway between
Margo and Leslie, scattering babies like confetti as she thumped on the cloth.
Thoroughly enraged at this treatment, the creature sped towards Leslie, her sting
quivering with emotion. Leslie leapt to his feat, overturning his chair, and flicked out
desperately with his napkin, sending the scorpion rolling across the cloth towards
Margo, who promptly let out a scream that any railway engine would have been
proud to produce. Mother, completely bewildered by this sudden and rapid change
from peace to chaos, put on her glasses and peered down the table to see what
was causing the pandemonium, and at that moment Margo, in a vain attempt to
stop the scorpion's advance, hurled a glass of water at it. The shower missed the
animal completely, but successfully drenched Mother, who, not being able to stand
cold water, promptly lost her breath and sat gasping at the end of the table, unable
even to protest. The scorpion had now gone to ground under Leslie's plate while
her babies swarmed wildly all over the table. Roger, mystified by the panic, but
determined to do his share, ran round and round the room, barking hysterically.

'It's that bloody boy again...' bellowed Larry.

'Look out! Look out! They're coming!' screamed Margo.

'All we need is a book,' roared Leslie; 'don't panic, hit 'em with a book.'

'What on earth's the *matter* with you all?' Mother kept imploring, mopping her glasses.

'It's that bloody boy... he'll kill the lot of us... Look at the table... knee deep in
scorpions...'

'Quick... quick... do something... Look out, look out!'

'Stop screeching and get a book, for God's sake... You're worse than the dog...
Shut *up*, Roger...'

'By the Grace of God I wasn't bitten...'

'Look out... there's another one... Quick... quick...'

'Oh, shut up and get me a book or something...'

'But *how* did the scorpions get on the table, dear?'

'That bloody boy... Every matchbox in the house is a deathtrap...'

'Look out, it's coming towards me... Quick, quick, do something...'

'Hit it with your knife... *your knife*... Go on, hit it...'

Since no one had bothered to explain things to him, Roger was under the
mistaken impression that the family were being attacked, and that it was his duty
to defend them. As Lugaretzia was the only stranger in the room, he came to the
logical conclusion that she must be the responsible party, so he bit her in the ankle.
This did not help matters very much.

By the time a certain amount of order had been restored, all the baby scorpions
had hidden themselves under various plates and bits of cutlery. Eventually, after
impassioned pleas on my part, backed up by Mother, Leslie's suggestion that the
whole lot be slaughtered was quashed. While the family, still simmering with rage
and fright, retired to the drawing-room, I spent half an hour rounding up the babies,
picking them up in a teaspoon, and returning them to their mother's back. Then I
carried them outside on a saucer and, with the utmost reluctance, released them on
the garden wall. Roger and I went and spent the afternoon on the hillside, for I felt it
would be prudent to allow the family to have a siesta before seeing them again.

From *My Family and Other Animals* by Gerald Durrell

Answer these questions.

1 Where did the author find the scorpions?

_____

2 Why was it 'unfortunate' that lunch was ready just as the author returned to the house?

_____

_____

3 Whose hand did the scorpion climb onto?

_____

4 What **simile** does the author use to show what happened to the baby scorpions when Larry flicked them with his napkin?

_____

5 What was Margo's scream compared to?

_____

6 How did Leslie propose to get rid of the scorpions?

_____

7–8 Give two reasons why the female scorpion was keen to get out of the matchbox.

_____

_____

9 How do you know that this was not the first time the author had kept creatures in matchboxes?

_____

10–11 Give two reasons why you can tell that Lugaretzia was not one of the family.

_____

_____

12–14 Explain these **phrases** in your own words.

(a)   'the mistaken impression' (lines 56–7)

_____

(b)   'vain attempt' (line 33)

_____

(c) 'gone to ground' (line 37)

_____

15 How do you know that getting the scorpions onto the saucer was a difficult job?

_____

_____

16 Why did the author think it was a good idea to spend the afternoon on the hillside?

_____

17–19 What does the description of collecting up the scorpions in the last paragraph tell you about the author's attitude to them? Give examples from the passage in your answer.

_____

_____

_____

20–21 What do these words mean?

'enraptured' (line 4) _____

'swarmed' (line 38) _____

22–24 Find three pieces of evidence in the passage which show you that the author was very interested in animals.

_____

_____

_____

25–26 In the dialogue section of the passage, the author rarely identifies the speakers. What impression does this give the reader?

_____

_____

26

E 2

Match each word with its **definition** as used in the passage.

27 surreptitiously _____ (a) unlucky

28 oblivious _____ (b) wise

29 rapidity	_____	(c) secretly
30 unfortunate	_____	(d) puzzled
31 bewildered	_____	(e) confusion
32 pandemonium	_____	(f) speed
33 imploring	_____	(g) dismissed
34 quashed	_____	(h) unaware
35 prudent	_____	(i) begging

9

E 2

Write a **homophone** for each of these words by adding a silent letter.

36 night	_____	37 rap	_____
38 retch	_____	39 new	_____
40 plum	_____	41 sent	_____
42 ring	_____	43 rite	_____

8

D 6

Underline the **verbs** in each **sentence**.

44 The family were having lunch.

45 He had been collecting insects for many years.

46 The family would have liked a peaceful meal.

47 The scorpion might have been killed.

48 He will hide his matchboxes in the future.

5

E 2

Complete each word with the **suffix** 'sure' or 'ture'.

49 disclo_____	50 tempera_____
51 lei_____	52 infrastruc_____
53 architec_____	54 carica_____
55 compo_____	56 manufac_____
57 cen_____	58 mois_____

10

Explain what these **expressions** mean.

59–60 to bite the hand that feeds you

_____

_____

61–62 to be hand in glove with someone

_____

_____

63–64 to hold the whip hand

_____

_____

65–66 to be a dab hand at something

_____

_____

67–68 to get the situation in hand

_____

_____

10

D 6

Replace the words in bold with a suitable **pronoun**.

69 The scorpion landed between **Margo and Leslie**.

_____

70 The matchbox belonged to **Larry**.

_____

71 **The scorpion** was agitated and annoyed.

_____

72 Roger bit **Lugaretzia**.

_____

73 He kept out of **the family's** way until later in the day.

_____

5

Write the **abstract noun** which can be made from each of these **adverbs**.

D 6

Adverb	Abstract noun
74 desperately	_____
75 completely	_____
76 promptly	_____
77 hysterically	_____
78 generously	_____

5

Write a word or **phrase** to explain the meaning of:

D 2

79 back down _____

80 back up _____

81 back off _____

82 back out _____

83 backbite _____

5

Add a **prefix** and a **suffix** to each **root word** to make a new word. Remember to make any necessary spelling changes.

E 2

Prefix	Root word	Suffix
84 _____	friendly	_____
85 _____	stress	_____
86 _____	turn	_____
87 _____	accurate	_____
88 _____	ordinary	_____
89 _____	move	_____

6

Complete each **sentence** with 'like' or 'as'.

90 Margo, _____ the rest of the family, was frightened of the scorpion.

91 Some creatures, such _____ scorpions, can be dangerous.

92 Some insects, such _____ bees, have stings.

93 He didn't stop bringing creatures into the house _____ he said he would.

94 _____ he expected, he was in a lot of trouble.

5

Write the word class of each word in bold.

95 I **scream** when I see a spider. _____

96 The **scream** echoed through the house. _____

97 He stayed indoors in the **cold** weather. _____

98 There is no cure for the common **cold**. _____

99 I **garden** at the weekend. _____

100 The **garden** wall was covered in insects. _____

6

Now go to the Progress Chart to record your score!   Total ◯ 100

Paper 7

The Darkling Thrush

I leant upon a coppice gate
   When Frost was spectre-grey,
And Winter's dregs made desolate
   The weakening eye of day.
The tangled bine-stems scored the sky   5
   Like strings of broken lyres,
And all mankind that haunted nigh
   Had sought their household fires.

The land's sharp features seemed to be
   The Century's corpse outleant,   10
His crypt the cloudy canopy,
   The wind his death-lament.
The ancient pulse of germ and birth
   Was shrunken hard and dry,
And every spirit upon earth   15
   Seemed fervourless as I.

At once a voice arose among
   The bleak twigs overhead
In a full-hearted evensong

Of joy illimited;   20
An aged thrush, frail, gaunt, and small,
    In blast-beruffled plume,
Had chosen thus to fling his soul
    Upon the growing gloom.

So little cause for carollings   25
    Of such ecstatic sound
Was written on terrestrial things
    Afar or nigh around,
That I could think there trembled through
    His happy good-night air   30
Some blessed Hope, whereof he knew
    And I was unaware.

by Thomas Hardy

Answer these questions.

1 At what time of the year is the poem set?

_____

2 How do you know that the poet is alone?

_____

3 Explain in your own words: 'The ancient pulse of germ and birth'.

_____

_____

4 What does the poet hear in 'the growing gloom'?

_____

5 Find two **adjectives** which the poet uses to describe the bird.

_____

6 Explain in your own words: 'Afar or nigh around'.

_____

7–8 At what time of the day is the poem set? Quote to support your answer.

_____

9–10 Explain these **phrases** in your own words:

(a) 'spectre-grey'

_____

(b) 'blast-beruffled plume'

_____

11–12 The poet describes himself as 'fervourless'. How do you think he is feeling?

_____

_____

13–14 At first, why is the poet puzzled by the sound he hears?

_____

_____

15–16 How does the poet explain the bird's joyful singing? Quote to support your answer.

_____

_____

17–19 The poem was written at the very end of the 19th century. Find three **phrases** in the poem which support this.

_____

_____

_____

20 Which **simile** does the poet use to describe the bine-stems?

_____

21–22 Write in your own words why the **simile** is effective.

_____

_____

23–25 The landscape affects the poet's mood. Pick out three words or **phrases** which show how gloomy the surroundings were.

_____

_____

_____

26–28 Find three **phrases** from the poem which show that the bird was feeling very differently from the poet.

_____

_____

_____ ◯ 28

E 2

Complete each word with 's' or 'c'.

29 analy_____e   **30** audien_____e

31 deci_____ion   **32** eviden_____e

33 ne_____essary   **34** sin_____erely

35 per_____pective   **36** re_____ipe

37 _____itizen   **38** sen_____or   ◯ 10

Explain what these **expressions** mean.

39–40 to sail close to the wind

_____

41–42 to get wind of something

_____

43–44 to get a second wind

_____

45–46 to whistle in the wind

_____

47–48 to take the wind out of someone's sails

_____ ◯ 10

D 2

Underline the **adverbial phrase** in each **sentence**.

49 I walked over the fields in the early evening.

50 The wind whistled through the trees with a low moan.

51 I saw a thrush sitting on the highest branch.

52 The bird sang loudly and joyfully.

53 It began to snow so I walked back in a hurry.   ◯ 5

Add the missing hyphen in each **sentence**.

54 Thomas Hardy is a world famous author.

55 He continued to write poetry until his mid eighties.

56 He built a strange looking house called Max Gate.

57 *The Darkling Thrush* is one of his best known poems.

58 Some people thought several of his stories were far fetched.

Complete each word with 'i' or 'y'.

59 ph_____sical   **60** acr_____lic

61 br_____ef   **62** d_____nasty

63 h_____giene   **64** pol_____ester

65 vitam_____n   **66** m_____th

67 rh_____me   **68** d_____namics

Match each word with its **definition** as used in the poem.

69 coppice   _____   (a) barren

70 desolate   _____   (b) thin and haggard

71 lyres   _____   (c) group of small trees

72 gaunt   _____   (d) of the earth

73 terrestrial   _____   (e) musical instruments

Circle the **adjective** in each group of four which is the *opposite* of the other three.

74 cloudy	overcast	grey	clear
75 abundant	plentiful	meagre	copious
76 ecstatic	doleful	delighted	joyful
77 infirm	robust	sturdy	stalwart
78 rich	wealthy	destitute	affluent

Make each word into its opposite by adding a **prefix**.

79 legal   _____   80 mature   _____

81 natural   _____   82 numerable   _____

83 regular   _____   84 moral   _____

85 legible   _____   86 rational   _____

87 mobile   _____   88 logical   _____   ⟨10⟩

Change these **sentences** from **singular** to **plural**.

89 I leant upon a coppice gate.

_____

90 He was unhappy and lonely in the field.

_____

91 The bird sang his song from high in the tree.

_____

92 The poet does not know why the bird is singing so ecstatically.

_____   ⟨4⟩

Circle the correct form of the word in brackets in each **sentence**.

93 My (advise/advice) is to stay away from the car park.

94 I (advise/advice) you to have breakfast before you go.

95 The permit will (license/licence) you to fish for the day.

96 The (license/licence) will let you fish for the day.

97 You can (practise/practice) for the match on Friday.

98 Choir (practise/practice) will be at six.

99 The ancient (prophecy/prophesy) predicted terrible plagues.

100 The wizard comes here to (prophecy/prophesy).   ⟨8⟩

Now go to the Progress Chart to record your score!   Total ⟨100⟩

This extract from Lorna Doone *describes when farmers had to go out and rescue sheep buried under heavy snowfalls.*

It must have snowed most wonderfully to have made that depth of covering in about eight hours. For one of Master Stickles' men, who had been out all the night, said that no snow began to fall until nearly midnight. And here it was, blocking up the doors, stopping the ways, and the water-courses, and making it very much worse to walk than in a saw-pit newly used. However we trudged along in a line; I first,   5
and the other men after me; trying to keep my track, but finding legs and strength not up to it. Most of all, John Fry was groaning; certain that his time was come, and sending messages to his wife, and blessings to his children. For all this time it was snowing harder than it ever had snowed before, so far as a man might guess at it; and the leaden depth of the sky came down, like a mine turned upside down   10
on us. Not that the flakes were so very large; for I have seen much larger flakes in a shower of March, while sowing peas; but that there was no room between them, neither any relaxing, nor any change of direction.

Watch, like a good and faithful dog, followed us cheerfully, leaping out of the depth, which took him over his back and ears already, even in the level places;   15
while in the drifts he might have sunk to any distance out of sight, and never found his way up again. However, we helped him now and then, especially through the gaps and gateways, and so after a deal of floundering, some laughter and a little swearing, we all came safe to the lower meadow, where most of our flock was hurdled.

But behold, there was no flock at all! None, I mean, to be seen anywhere, only   20
at one corner of the field, by the eastern end, where the snow drove in, a great white billow, as high as a barn and as broad as a house... And all the while from the smothering sky, more and more fiercely at every blast, came the pelting pitiless arrows, winged with murky white, and pointed with barbs of frost.

But although, for people who had no sheep, the sight was a very fine one (so   25
far at least as the weather permitted any sight at all); yet for us, with our flock beneath it, this great mount had but little charm. Watch began to scratch at once, and to howl along the side of it; he knew that his charge was buried there, and his business taken from him. But we four men set to in earnest, digging with all our might and main, shovelling away at the great white pile, and fetching it into the   30
meadow. Each man made for himself a cave, scooping at the soft cold flux, which slid upon him at every stroke, and throwing it out behind him, in piles of castled fancy. At last we drove our tunnels in (for we worked indeed for the lives of us), and all converging towards the middle, held our tools and listened.

From *Lorna Doone* by R D Blackmore

Answer these questions.

1 At what time had the snow started to fall?

_____

2 Find two **adjectives** which the author uses to describe Watch.

_____

3 What is the **collective noun** for a group of sheep?

_____

4 Where were the farmers going to look for their sheep?

_____

5 How many farmers were going to look for their sheep?

_____

6–7 What time is it at the beginning of the passage?

_____

8 The narrator says that the other men were 'trying to keep my track' (line 6). What were the other men doing and why?

_____

9 John Fry was 'certain that his time had come'. What does this mean?

_____

10–11 Find two **similes** which the author uses to describe the 'great, white billow'.

_____

12–13 What is the difference between the snow in this passage and the snow in early spring?

_____

14 How can you tell that the men's walk was not completely miserable?

_____

15 Where did the author think the flock was in the field?

_____

16 When the men stopped digging, what were they listening for?

_____

17–19 What do these **phrases** mean?

'a deal of floundering' (line 18)   _____

'our flock was hurdled' (line 19)   _____

'neither any relaxing' (line 13)   _____

20–21 Find two descriptions of the snow which suggest that the narrator thought of it as a weapon being hurled at them.

_____

_____

22–23 Why do you think so much snow was a fine sight 'for people who had no sheep'?

_____

_____

24–25 How do you know that the snow was falling so heavily that the farmers had difficulty in seeing? Find two **phrases** that show this.

_____

_____

26 What does the narrator mean when he says 'for we worked for the very lives of us'?

_____

_____

27–30 How is Watch feeling when:

(a)   they set off to look for the sheep?

(b)   they reached the corner of the field?

Quote from the passage to support your answer.

(a)   _____

_____

(b)   _____

_____

31–32 What does the author mean when he says that Watch 'knew that his charge was buried there, and his business taken from him' (lines 28–9)?

_____

_____

33–35 Explain in your own words how the farmers tried to dig out the sheep.

_____

_____

_____

35

50

Circle the unstressed vowels in each word.

36 business _____

37 estuary _____

38 interest _____

39 laboratory _____

40 hygiene _____

41 circumference _____

42 ferocious _____

43 parliament _____

44 marriage _____

45 literature _____

10

Complete each **expression** with a **preposition**.

D 6

46 Can I depend _____ you?

47 I am satisfied _____ my work.

48 He had a good ear _____ music.

49 She was worthy _____ great praise.

50 She decided to confide _____ her friend.

5

Make an **adjective** from each of these **nouns**.

D 6

51 snow _____

52 frost _____

53 strength _____

54 depth _____

55 distance _____

56 charm _____

57 cavern _____

58 cylinder _____

59 burden _____

60 apathy _____

10

Explain what these **expressions** mean.

61–62 as cold as ice

_____

63–64 a cold-blooded person

_____

65–66 to give someone the cold shoulder

_____

67–68 to pour cold water on something

_____

69–70 to give cold comfort

_____

◯ 10

E 2

Match each word with the correct **definition**.

71 consent	_____	(a)	come together
72 concentrate	_____	(b)	move towards each other
73 converge	_____	(c)	agree to
74 concur	_____	(d)	agree with
75 convene	_____	(e)	give attention to

◯ 5

E 2

Complete each word with the correct vowel.

76 choc_____late   **77** libr_____ry

78 second_____ry   **79** cemet_____ry

80 maint_____nance   **81** asp_____rin

82 rhinocer_____s   **83** resta_____rant

84 b_____oyant   **85** mack_____rel

◯ 10

Change each of the active sentences into passive sentences.

D 1

86 Master Sickles watched the snow.

_____

87 The wind blew the snow into drifts.

_____

88 Each man dug a hole in the snow.

_____

89 The snow had buried the sheep.

_____

90 The other men followed me.

_____

5

Write a **homophone** for each of these words.

E 2

91 stair   _____

92 beech   _____

93 paws   _____

94 birth   _____

95 draft   _____

5

Rewrite the passage in the context of the extract, adding the missing apostrophes.

D 5

96–100 The farmers sheep had been buried by the heavy snowfall. Theyd set out to find them. All that could be heard were the dogs barks and the mens heavy breathing as they ploughed through the deep snow. They couldnt help fearing the worst.

_____

_____

_____

_____

5

I wandered lonely as a cloud

I wandered lonely as a cloud
That floats on high o'er vales and hills,
When all at once I saw a crowd,
A host of golden daffodils;
Beside the lake, beneath the trees,   5
Fluttering and dancing in the breeze.

Continuous as the stars that shine
And twinkle on the milky way,
They stretched in never-ending line
Along the margin of the bay: 10
Ten thousand saw I at a glance,
Tossing their heads in sprightly dance.

The waves beside them danced; but they
Out-did the sparkling waves in glee:
A poet could not but be gay,   15
In such a jocund company:
I gazed – and gazed – but little thought
What wealth the show to me had brought:

For oft, when on my couch I lie
In vacant or in pensive mood,   20
They flash upon that inward eye
Which is the bliss of solitude;
And then my heart with pleasure fills,
And dances with the daffodils.

by William Wordsworth

Answer these questions.

1 Do you think the poet is walking in a town or in the countryside? Give a reason for your answer.

_____

_____

2 Find two **verbs** which show how the daffodils moved.

_____

3 What does the **phrase** 'never-ending' tell you about the daffodils?

_____

4 How many daffodils does the poet think he saw?

_____

5 What makes the poet's heart fill with 'pleasure'?

_____

6 Where exactly were the daffodils?

_____

7 What does the line 'Continuous as the stars that shine' (line 7) tell you about the daffodils?

_____

_____

8 What is the 'milky way' (line 8)?

_____

9–10 What does the poet mean when he says that the daffodils 'out-did' the waves?

_____

_____

11–12 How do you know that the poet spent a long time looking at the daffodils?

_____

_____

13 Find an example of a **simile** in the poem.

_____

14–16 What do these words and **phrases** in the poem mean?

'all at once' (line 3) _____

'vales' (line 2) _____

'bliss' (line 22) _____

17–18 Where is the poet when he thinks about the daffodils and what kind of state is he in?

_____

19–20 Explain in your own words how the poet makes the daffodils seem human. Give examples from the poem.

_____

_____

_____

21–22 In what way do you think the sight of the daffodils brought 'wealth' to the poet?

_____

_____

23–24 Explain what you think the poet means by 'inward eye'.

_____

_____

25–28 What did the poet feel about the daffodils:

(a)   when he first saw them? (*2 marks*)

(b)   when he thought about them later? (*2 marks*)

Quote from the poem to support your answer.

(a)   _____

_____

(b)   _____

_____

29–31 What do you think makes 'solitude' so blissful for the poet?

_____

_____

31

Write these old-fashioned words in full.

32 'twas   _____   **33** 'tis   _____

34 is't   _____   **35** o'er   _____

36 oft   _____

5

56

Complete each **sentence** with one of the following:

 lie **lay** **lain** **laid**

37 I like to _____ on the grass and look at the clouds.

38 I _____ down because I had a headache.

39 Dad asked me to _____ the table.

40 The army _____ down its weapons.

41 The old watch must have _____ in the drawer for years.

5

Add 'ou' or 'ow' to complete each word.

42 sh_____ld **43** sh_____er

44 tr_____el **45** d_____ble

46 m_____ntain **47** sc_____l

48 pr_____led **49** b_____ntiful

50 c_____gar **51** g_____lash

10

Circle the **definition** which is closest in meaning to the word in bold as it is used in the poem.

52 host

 (a) person who invites guests to their house

 (b) large number

 (c) person who introduces a television show

53 margin

 (a) the area around the edge of something

 (b) the empty space at the side of a page

 (c) an amount of space that is more than you need

54 sprightly

 (a) goblin-like

 (b) mournful

 (c) lively

55 glee

    (a)   soft light

    (b)   happiness

    (c)   spite

56 gay

    (a)   happy

    (b)   thoughtful

    (c)   sad

57 jocund

    (a)   large

    (b)   merry

    (c)   colourful

58 show

    (a)   entertainment

    (b)   walk

    (c)   sight

59 vacant

    (a)   empty-headed

    (b)   thinking about nothing in particular

    (c)   sorrowful

60 pensive

    (a)   thoughtful

    (b)   having money

    (c)   angry

61 solitude

    (a)   the state of being abandoned

    (b)   the state of being alone

    (c)   the state of being miserable

10

Make an **adverb** from each of these **adjectives**.

62 vacant   _____

63 pensive   _____

64 repeated   _____

65 playful   _____

66 scornful   _____

67 cool   _____

68 gay   _____

69 noble   _____

70 clumsy   _____

71 weary   _____

10

Explain what these **expressions** mean.

72–73 every cloud has a silver lining

_____

74–75 to be under a cloud

_____

76–77 to have one's head in the clouds

_____

78–79 to be on cloud nine

_____

80–81 to cast a cloud over

_____

10

Change each of the **sentences** from **direct** to **reported speech**.

82 'I wandered lonely as a cloud,' said the poet.

_____

83 'Where did you walk?' asked his friend.

_____

84 The poet replied, 'I went over by the lake.'

_____

85 'Were the daffodils in bloom?' asked his friend.

_____

86 'Yes. Thousands of them,' the poet said. 'They looked magnificent.'

_____

5

Use a hyphenated compound adjective to complete each **sentence**.

D 1
D 6

87 A person who works hard is a _____ _____ person.

88 Biscuits covered in chocolate are _____ _____ biscuits.

89 Medicine with an evil smell is an _____ _____ medicine.

90 A golf course with eighteen holes is an _____ _____ golf course.

91 A bottle that holds two litres is a _____ _____ bottle.

5

Write an **antonym** for each word by adding a **prefix**.

D 9
E 2

92 kind _____

93 wise _____

94 certain _____

95 possible _____

96 continue _____

97 accurate _____

98 regular _____

99 mature _____

100 natural _____

9

Now go to the Progress Chart to record your score!   Total   10(

This extract from Henry V *by William Shakespeare takes place on the eve of battle.*
The English are about to face the French. The Duke of Westmoreland suggests that
they need a bigger army. King Henry replies…

If we are mark'd to die, we are enow	
To do our country loss; and if to live,	
The fewer men the greater share of honour.	
God's will! I pray thee, wish not one man more.	
By Jove, I am not covetous for gold;	5
Nor care I who doth feed upon my cost:	
It yearns me not if men my garments wear;	
Such outward things dwell not in my desires:	
But if it be a sin to covet honour,	
I am the most offending soul alive.	10
No, faith, my coz, wish not a man from England:	
God's peace! I would not lose so great an honour,	
As one man more, methinks, would share from me,	
For the best hope I have. O do not wish one more!	
Rather proclaim it, Westmoreland, through my host,	15
That he which hath no stomach to this fight,	
Let him depart; his passport shall be made,	
And crowns for convoy put into his purse:	
We would not die in that man's company	
That fears his fellowship to die with us.	20
This day is call'd the Feast of Crispian:	
He that outlives this day, and comes safe home,	
Will stand a tip-toe when this day is nam'd,	
And rouse him at the name of Crispian.	
He that shall live this day, and see old age,	25
Will yearly on the vigil feast his neighbours,	
And say, To-morrow is Saint Crispian:	
Then will he strip his sleeve and show his scars,	
And say, These wounds I had on Crispin's day.	
Old men forget; yet all shall be forgot,	30
But he'll remember with advantages	
What feats he did that day: then shall our names,	
Familiar in their mouths as household words, –	
Harry the King, Bedford and Exeter,	
Warwick and Talbot, Salisbury and Gloster –	35
Be in their flowing cups freshly remember'd.	
This story shall the good man teach his son;	
And Crispin Crispian shall ne'er go by,	
From this day to the ending of the world, –	
But we in it shall be remember'd,	40
We few, we happy few, we band of brothers;	
For he to-day that sheds his blood with me	

Shall be my brother; be he ne'er so vile,
This day shall gentle his condition:
And gentlemen in England now a-bed   45
Shall think themselves accurs'd they were not here,
And hold their manhoods cheap whiles any speaks
That fought with us upon Saint Crispin's day.

Answer these questions.

1 Who is King Henry talking to?

_____

2 The men who go home will be given 'crowns' (line 18). What does this mean?

_____

3 What feast day is it?

_____

4 Why does the King think that his name and those of Bedford, Exeter, Warwick,
  Talbot, Salisbury and Gloster will be remembered?

_____

_____

5 How will 'gentlemen in England now a-bed' (line 45) feel when the battle is
  talked of in the future?

_____

_____

6 Explain the meaning of: 'If we are mark'd to die' (line 1).

_____

_____

7 How do you know that the King is not bothered about being rich? Give evidence
  from the text.

_____

_____

8 Explain the **expression**: 'no stomach to this fight' (line 16).

_____

_____

9–11 What do these words mean?

'enow' (line 1) _____

'covetous' (line 5) _____

'methinks' (line 13) _____

12 On the anniversary of the battle, a soldier who fought with the King will 'feast his neighbours' (line 26). What does this mean?

_____

_____

13–14 What will the difference be in the future between most old men and those old men who fought in the battle when they were young?

_____

_____

15–16 Explain in your own words whom Henry will consider his 'brother'.

_____

_____

17–18 Explain what the King means when he says: 'The fewer men the greater share of honour'.

_____

_____

19–21 Henry says, 'Rather proclaim it, Westmoreland, through my host'.

Explain in your own words:

(a) what Henry wants proclaimed.

_____

_____

(b) to whom he wants Westmoreland to 'proclaim it'.

_____

_____

22–24 Explain in your own words how those who fought and came 'safe home' will behave, each year, on the anniversary of the battle.

_____

_____

25–27 Explain in your own words why the King calls those with him, 'We few, we happy few' (line 41).

_____

_____

28–30 Henry could be considered a brave man or a foolish man for the same reason. Why?

_____

_____

30

D 10

Write these **abbreviations** in full.

31 St. Christopher   _____

32 Dr. Green   _____

33 Prof. West   _____

34 Lieut. Sharp   _____

35 Rev. Jones   _____

5

E 2

Complete each **sentence** with 'less' or 'fewer'.

36 I wish you would make _____ noise!

37 Please put _____ water in the kettle.

38 There are _____ members of the club this year.

39 You have been _____ successful this time.

40 We have had _____ sunny days this month than last month.

5

Match each word with its correct **definition** as used in Henry's speech. Write the correct number in the space.

E 2

41 covet   _____   (a) travel

42 offending   _____   (b) humble

64

43 convoy	_____	(c)	desire
44 feats	_____	(d)	sinning
45 vile	_____	(e)	deeds

D 6

Make **abstract nouns** from these **adjectives**.

Adjective	Abstract noun
46 victorious	_____
47 strong	_____
48 grateful	_____
49 wise	_____
50 honourable	_____
51 valiant	_____
52 heroic	_____
53 cowardly	_____
54 patriotic	_____
55 humble	_____

D 1
D 2

Rewrite each **sentence** with the **adverbial clause** at the beginning.

56 King Henry and his army won the battle because they fought bravely.

_____

57 Henry talked with his soldiers before the battle.

_____

58 The soldiers were frightened when the French army advanced.

_____

59 The King was confident although his army was very small.

_____

60 The armies agreed a truce in order to tend to the wounded.

_____

Explain what these **expressions** mean.

61–62 to be in the wars

_____

63–64 to be on the warpath

_____

65–66 to have a fighting chance

_____

67–68 to fight shy of

_____

69–70 to have a pyrrhic victory

_____

10

E 2

Add 'ous', 'ious', or 'eous' to complete each word.

71 court_____   **72** ser_____

73 outrag_____   **74** continu_____

75 consc_____   **76** contag_____

77 victor_____   **78** prosper_____

79 simultan_____   **80** miscellan_____

10

D 12

Rewrite each of these **reported speech sentences** as **direct speech**.

81–82 King Henry said that he didn't care about wealth but he did care about honour.

_____

_____

83–84 Westmoreland asked how they could win against the huge French army.

_____

_____

85–86 The King said that his soldiers must listen to him. If any of them wanted to go home, they could go now.

_____

_____

87–88 Bedford shouted that if any soldier left the battlefield, he would be branded a coward.

_____

_____

89–90 King Henry promised that all who fought with him on Saint Crispin's day would be remembered for ever.

_____

_____

○ 10

E 2

Fill the gaps to complete the spelling of each word.

91 campai___n

92 parl___ament

93 ex___aust

94 reli___nt

95 vac___um

96 substan___ial

97 b___oyant

98 auxil___ary

99 mis___letoe

100 rhod___dendron

○ 10

Progress Chart   English 12⁺-13⁺ years

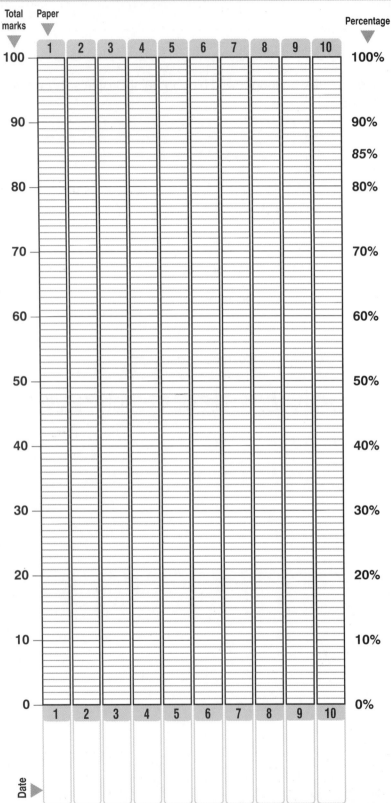

Total marks

Paper

Percentage

| 1 | 2 | 3 | 4 | 5 | 6 | 7 | 8 | 9 | 10 |

100 — 100%

90 — 90%

85%

80 — 80%

70 — 70%

60 — 60%

50 — 50%

40 — 40%

30 — 30%

20 — 20%

10 — 10%

0 — 0%

| 1 | 2 | 3 | 4 | 5 | 6 | 7 | 8 | 9 | 10 |

Date

When you've finished the book use the Next Steps Planner ➤